T0084439

Joseph Haydn

Symphony No. 101 in D major / D-Dur
Hob. I:101 'The Clock'

Edited by / Herausgegeben von
Harry Newstone

EULENBURG

EAS 157
ISBN 978-3-7957-6557-6
ISMN 979-0-2002-2545-7

© 2009 Ernst Eulenburg & Co GmbH, Mainz
for Europe excluding the British Isles
Ernst Eulenburg Ltd, London
for all other countries
Edition based on Eulenburg Study Score ETP 439
CD ℗ & © 1989 Naxos Rights International Ltd

Ernst Eulenburg Ltd
48 Great Marlborough Street
London W1F 7BB

Contents / Inhalt

Preface   V

Vorwort   VIII

I.   Adagio   1   Track 1

Presto   3

II.   Andante   30   Track 2

III. Menuetto/Trio. Allegretto 48 Track ③

IV. Finale. Vivace 59 Track ④

Preface

Composed: 1794 in London
First performance: 3 March 1794 in London
Original publisher: André, Offenbach, 1799
Instrumentation: 2 Flutes, 2 Oboes, 2 Clarinets, 2 Bassoons –
2 Horns, 2 Trumpets – Timpani – Strings
Duration: ca. 28 minutes

In the autumn of 1790 Prince Nikolaus Joseph Esterházy, Haydn's employer and patron, died and his son, Prince Paul Anton, succeeded him. Almost at once the great (but considerably expensive) musical establishment which had for nearly thirty years nurtured the composer, and is now chiefly remembered for the glory he brought to it, was dismantled. Although still nominally Capellmeister, with a yearly pension, Haydn was at last free to travel wherever he wished, something he had not been able to do before. He returned to Vienna relieved of the daily pressures of court duties, but his respite was not to last long. Johann Peter Salomon, the German-born violinist and London impresario, was visiting Cologne when he heard of the death of Prince Nikolaus and lost no time in getting to Vienna determined to procure Haydn for his forthcoming London season. It was not the first time he had invited Haydn to England; now the composer was free to accept, and he did. A contract was exchanged and the two left Vienna in the middle of December and arrived in Dover on New Year's Day 1791.

Haydn stayed in England for a year and a half and returned for a second visit of similar duration in 1794-5. The stimulus he received from the London musical scene, the reception he was accorded there and the high quality of the musicians placed at his disposal inspired him to some of his finest music. The twelve symphonies he wrote for Salomon (six for each visit) are the summation of his orchestral achievement and the ground upon which the music he composed after his return to Vienna – notably the last six masses, *The Creation* and *The Seasons* – was based.

The most popular of the London symphonies are among the most frequently played of Haydn's works, yet for very many years they were (and often still are) performed from texts that had, during the 19th century, become seriously corrupted from the originals. The first modern attempt to present a uniform set of scores based upon authentic sources came with Ernst Praetorius's edition for Eulenberg in the 1930s. For this he consulted the autograph scores of Nos. 98, 99, 101, 102, 103 and 104 but not those of Nos. 94, 95, 96 and 100 (No. 93 has disappeared and the whereabouts of No.97 was then unknown). One can only speculate on why Praetorius was not able to examine the autograph of No. 94 which was in the then

Preußische Staatsbibliothek in Berlin, where he had seen those of Nos. 98, 99, 101, 102 and 104, or Nos. 95 and 96 which were in the British Museum along with No. 103 of which he had received a photocopy. Clearly, detailed knowledge of the whereabouts of Haydn autographs was still very sketchy in the 1930s and Praetorius probably had no way of knowing what we, with the benefit of a further 50 years of Haydn research, can take for granted. Thus Praetorius's edition, while the best available at the time and certainly an important step in the right direction was, not surprisingly, uneven.

The phase of Haydn research that was to result in no less than a renaissance was now well begun. In 1939 the distinguished Danish scholar Jens Peter Larsen published *Die Haydn-Überlieferung* and two years later a facsimile print of *Drei Haydn-Kataloge*, revealing for the first time the immensity of the subject. The post-war years saw the formation in London of the Haydn Orchestra and in Boston of the Haydn Society (both 1949). In 1954, the founder of the Haydn Society, H.C. Robbins Landon, in an article *The original versions of Haydn's first 'Salomon' symphonies*, drew our attention to the extent to which the standard performing editions of these works (mostly Breitkopf & Härtel and Peters) were in many cases 'flagrant falsifications of Haydn's own texts'. For a discussion on how these alterations came about the reader is referred to that article as well as to Landon's *The Symphonies of Joseph Haydn*, and his *Haydn – Chronicle and Works*, Vol. 3 *Haydn in England*.

Since the mid-1950s Henle Verlag, Munich, has issued a number of volumes of Haydn symphonies as part of a Complete Edition of his works for the Haydn Institute of Cologne. Universal Edition, Vienna, issued all the symphonies during the 1960s in an edition by H. C. Robbins Landon.

In 1959, the present writer, with material and advice from Professor Landon, revised and conducted all the London symphonies in a series of BBC broadcasts commemorating the 150th anniversary of the composer's death. The aim was to get as close as possible to Haydn's original intentions not only from the scholar's point of view but from the performer's too.

The texts were accordingly prepared from a number of manuscript sources of primary authenticity and one early printed edition of unusual interest and importance.

Symphony No. 101

This symphony was composed for Haydn's second visit to London in 1794/5 for which he had been commissioned by Salomon to provide, among other music, six new symphonies – as he had done for his first visit in 1791/2. In the event, the first three of these new symphonies (Nos. 99–101) were to be the last of the 'London' symphonies presented at Salomon's Hanover Square concerts, for in January 1795 the violinist/impresario announced that he was 'under the necessity, from circumstances which he has it not in his power to control, to decline the further continuance of the establishment'.[1]

---

[1] H. C. Robbins Landon, *Haydn – Chronicle and Works* (vol. III *Haydn in England*), London, 1976, 280

The Symphony No. 101 was given its first performance, with Salomon as leader and Haydn at the piano, on 3 March at the fourth concert of Salomon's 1794 season in the Hanover Square Rooms, and it was repeated at the fifth concert a week later. The work was an immediate success and it has remained to this day one of Haydn's most brilliant and popular symphonies. The autograph score of both this symphony and of No. 100 ('The Military') are dated 1794, but it seems likely that all or part of No. 101 was composed first, since its minuet was written on the same (Italian) paper that Haydn hat used for the Symphony No. 99 the previous year in Vienna.[2] The title 'The Clock', which the symphony gained from the tick-tock accompaniment that pervades the second movement, was not attached to the work until sometime in the nineteenth century.[3]

Harry Newstone

[2] ibid., 492
[3] ibid.

Vorwort

komponiert: 1794 in London
Uraufführung: 3. März 1794 in London
Originalverlag: André, Offenbach, 1799
Orchesterbesetzung: 2 Flöten, 2 Oboen, 2 Klarinetten, 2 Fagotte –
2 Hörner, 2 Trompeten – Pauken – Streicher
Spieldauer: etwa 28 Minuten

Im Herbst 1790 starb Fürst Nikolaus Joseph Esterházy, Haydns Dienstherr und Gönner; Fürst Paul Anton, sein Sohn, folgte ihm nach. Fast unmittelbar hierauf wurde das bedeutende, allerdings ziemlich kostspielige Musikleben am Hofe eingestellt, das Haydn nahezu dreißig Jahre lang ernährt hatte und an das man sich heute hauptsächlich des Glanzes wegen erinnert, den es durch den Komponisten erhalten hatte. Obwohl er auch weiterhin den Kapellmeistertitel führen durfte und eine jährliche Pension erhielt, konnte Haydn im Gegensatz zu früher nun schließlich nach Belieben reisen. Er kehrte nach Wien zurück, entlastet vom täglichen Zwang des Dienstes am Hofe – jedoch sollte diese Ruhepause nicht von langer Dauer sein. Als der deutschstämmige Geiger und Londoner Impresario Johann Peter Salomon während eines Aufenthaltes in Köln vom Tod des Fürsten Nikolaus erfuhr, eilte er unverzüglich nach Wien, entschlossen, Haydn für die kommende Saison nach London zu verpflichten. Dies war nicht das erste Mal, dass er Haydn nach England eingeladen hatte; jetzt jedoch war der Komponist in der Lage zuzusagen, und er tat es auch. Ein Vertrag wurde ausgehandelt und die beiden verließen Wien Mitte Dezember und erreichten Dover am Neujahrstag 1791.

Haydn blieb anderthalb Jahre lang in England und kehrte 1794/95 zu einem zweiten, etwa gleich langen Aufenthalt zurück. Die Anregungen, die er durch das Londoner Musikleben erhielt, die Aufnahme dort und die hohe Qualität der ihm zur Verfügung stehenden Musiker inspirierten ihn zu mehreren seiner bedeutendsten Werke. So bilden die zwölf Sinfonien für Salomon (sechs für jeden Aufenthalt) die Zusammenfassung seiner ganzen Kunst der Orchesterkomposition und die Grundlage für die Werke, die er nach seiner Rückkehr nach Wien schrieb – vor allem die sechs letzten Messen sowie die *Schöpfung* und die *Jahreszeiten*.

Die bekanntesten der Londoner Sinfonien gehören zu den meistgespielten Werken Haydns, jedoch wurden sie viele Jahre lang (vielfach noch bis in die heutige Zeit) aus Notenmaterial aufgeführt, das im 19. Jahrhundert gegenüber dem Originaltext erheblich verfälscht worden war. Den ersten neueren Versuch, aufgrund der authentischen Quellen einen einheitlichen Satz Partituren herauszubringen, stellt die Ausgabe von Ernst Praetorius im Rahmen der

Edition Eulenberg in den 1930er Jahren dar. Er zog die Partitur-Autographe von Nr. 98, 99, 101, 102, 103 und 104 heran. Nicht aber diejenigen von Nr. 94, 95, 96 und 100 (das Autograph von Nr. 93 ist verschollen, und das von Nr. 97 war damals nicht nachweisbar). Man kann nur Vermutungen darüber anstellen, warum Praetorius nicht in der Lage war, das Autograph von Nr. 94 zu untersuchen, das in der damaligen Preußischen Staatsbibliothek in Berlin lag, wo er auch die Autographe von Nr. 98, 99, 101, 102 und 104 eingesehen hatte; Nr. 95 und 96 waren ihm im British Museum London zugänglich, zusammen mit dem Autograph von Nr. 103, das ihm als Fotokopie vorlag. Auf jeden Fall war die Kenntnis der Aufbewahrungsorte von Haydn-Autographen in den 1930er Jahren noch sehr lückenhaft und Praetorius konnte damals wohl kaum wissen, was wir heute, nach weiteren 50 Jahren Haydn-Forschung, als erwiesen betrachten können. So war es nicht verwunderlich, dass die Ausgaben von Praetorius in sich uneinheitlich waren, auch wenn sie zu ihrer Zeit die besten verfügbaren waren und sicherlich einen Schritt in die richtige Richtung unternahmen.

Damit hatte eine Zeit intensiver Haydn-Forschung begonnen, die eine regelrechte Renaissance auslöste. 1939 veröffentlichte der bedeutende dänische Musikwissenschaftler Jens Peter Larsen sein Buch *Die Haydn-Überlieferung* und zwei Jahre später als Faksimile *Drei Haydn-Kataloge*; damit wies er erstmals auf die nahezu unüberschaubaren Dimensionen dieses Forschungsbereichs hin. In den Nachkriegsjahren folgten die Gründung des Haydn-Orchesters London und in Bosten die der Haydn-Gesellschaft (beide 1949), 1954 machte H. C. Robbins Landon, Begründer der Haydn-Gesellschaft, in einem Aufsatz *The original versions of Haydn's first 'Salomon' symphonies* auf das Ausmaß aufmerksam, in dem das verfügbare Aufführungsmaterial dieser Werke (hauptsächlich von Breitkopf & Härtel und Peters) in vielen Fällen durch „offenkundige Verfälschung von Haydn's eigenem Notentext" entstellt war. Bezüglich einer eingehenden Darstellung, wie es zu diesen Abweichungen kam, sei hier auf den Aufsatz sowie auf Landons Arbeiten *The Symphonies of Joseph Haydn* und *Haydn – Chronicle and Works* (Bd. 3 *Haydn in England*) hingewiesen.

Seit Mitte der 1950er Jahre hat der Henle-Verlag München im Rahmen einer Gesamtausgabe der Werke Haydns durch das Haydn-Institut Köln mehrere Bände mit Sinfonien veröffentlicht. Bei der Universal Edition Wien erschienen alle Sinfonien in den 1960er Jahren in einer Ausgabe von H. C. Robbins Landon.

1959 revidierte der Herausgeber der hier vorliegenden Ausgabe anlässlich einer Sendereihe der BBC zum 150. Todestage des Komponisten, in der er selbst alle Londoner Sinfonien Haydns dirigierte, die Partituren, wofür ihm Robbins Landon eigenes Material und seinen Rat zur Verfügung stellte. Das Ziel war, Haydns eigenen Intentionen nicht nur vom wissenschaftlichen Standpunkt aus, sondern auch aus der Sicht des ausübenden Musikers so nahe wie möglich zu kommen.

Der Notentext wurde aufgrund einer Anzahl handschriftlicher Primärquellen und einer besonders interessanten und wichtigen Druckausgabe erarbeitet.

Sinfonie Nr. 101

Haydn komponierte diese Sinfonie aus Anlass seines zweiten Londoner Aufenthaltes 1794/95. In Salomons Auftrag sollte er, wie bei seinem ersten Aufenthalt 1791/92, neben anderen Kompositionen eine Folge von sechs neuen Sinfonien komponieren. Letzten Endes waren die ersten drei dieser neuen Sinfonien (Nr. 99–101) die letzten der „Londoner Sinfonien", die im Rahmen von Salomons Konzertreihe im Hanover Square dargeboten wurden. Im Januar 1795 nämlich hatte der Geiger und Impresario Salomon bekannt gegeben, dass er sich aufgrund von Umständen, die sich seinem Zugriff entzögen, gezwungen sähe, dieses Unternehmen nicht mehr weiter fortzuführen.[1]

Die Uraufführung der Sinfonie Nr. 101 fand am 3. März als viertes „Salomon-Konzert" der Spielzeit 1794 in den Hanover Square Rooms statt. Salomon hatte die Konzertmeisterposition inne, Haydn saß am Cembalo. Im fünften Konzert, eine Woche später, fand eine Wiederholung statt. Das Werk errang einen spontanen Erfolg und zählt bis in die heutige Zeit zu Haydns herausragenden und auch populärsten Sinfonien. Die autographe Partitur trägt ebenso wie die Sinfonie Nr. 100 („Militär-Sinfonie") das Datum 1794. Es ist hingegen wahrscheinlicher, dass die Sinfonie Nr. 101 ganz oder teilweise zuvor komponiert wurde, denn Haydn schrieb ihr Menuett auf demselben (aus Italien stammenden) Papier nieder, das er im vorangegangenen Jahr in Wien für die Sinfonie Nr. 99 benutzt hatte.[2] Der Name „Die Uhr" – eine Anspielung auf die „Tick-tack-Begleitfigur", die den zweiten Satz durchzieht – wurde dem Werk erst im Laufe des 19. Jahrhunderts beigegeben.[3]

Harry Newstone

.

---

[1] H. C. Robbins Landon, *Haydn – Chronicle and Works* (vol. III *Haydn in England*), London, 1976, S. 280.
[2] Ibid. S. 492
[3] Ibid.

Symphony No. 101
'The Clock'

Joseph Haydn
(1732–1809)
Hob. I:101

I. Adagio

EAS 157

Edited by Harry Newstone
© 2009 Ernst Eulenburg Ltd, London
and Ernst Eulenburg & Co GmbH, Mainz

Presto

14

24

II. Andante

48

III. Menuetto

Allegretto

50

Trio

55

Menuet Da Capo

IV. Finale

Vivace

62

64

Laus Deo